KEEP CALM
AND
COLOUR
CATS

HUCK &
PUCKER

The idea of calm exists
in a sitting cat.

Jules Renard

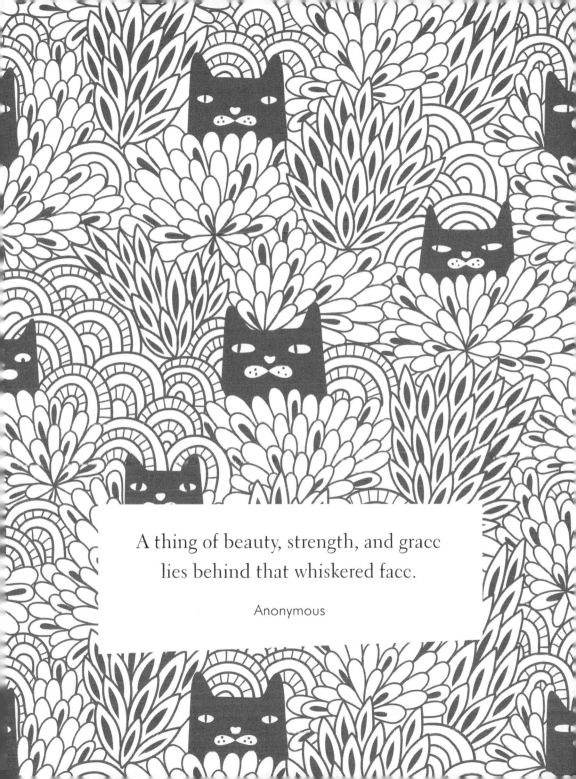

A thing of beauty, strength, and grace
lies behind that whiskered face.

Anonymous

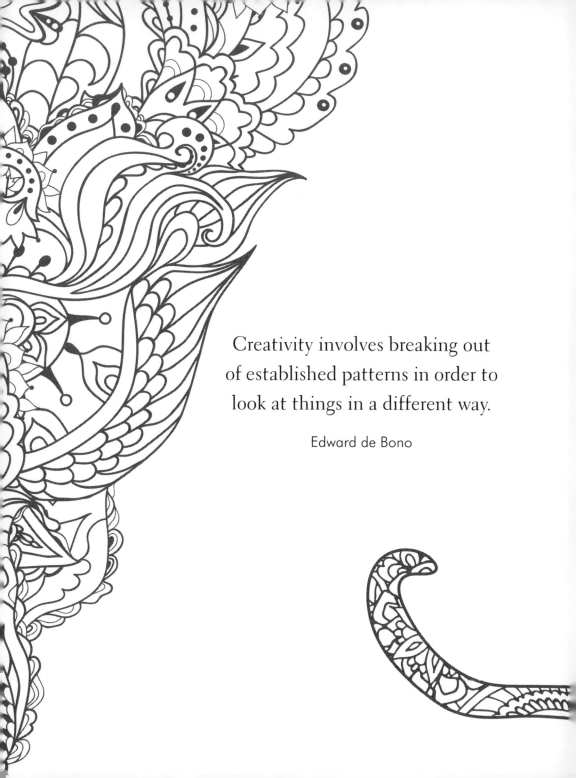

Creativity involves breaking out
of established patterns in order to
look at things in a different way.

Edward de Bono

Cats are intended to teach us that not
everything in nature has a purpose.

Garrison Keillor

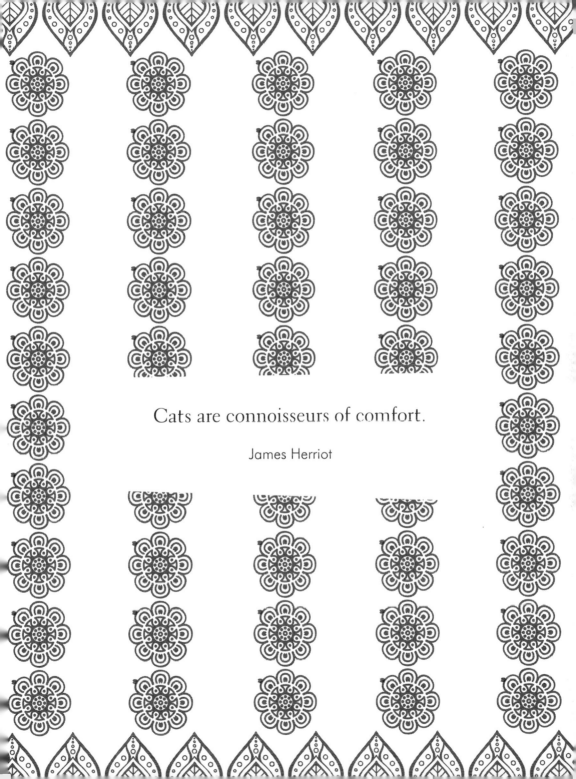

Cats are connoisseurs of comfort.

James Herriot

I have studied many philosophers
and many cats. The wisdom of
cats is infinitely superior.

Hippolyte Taine

To draw, you must close
your eyes and sing.

Pablo Picasso

You cannot look at a sleeping
cat and feel tense.

Jane Pauley

Cats are gloriously human.

L. M. Montgomery

I have lived with several Zen masters – all of them cats.

Eckhart Tolle

Like emotions, colours
are a reflection of life.

Janice Glennaway

When they are among us,
cats are angels.

George Sand

There are few things in life
more heart-warming than to
be welcomed by a cat.

Tay Hohoff

Time spent with cats
is never wasted.

May Sarton

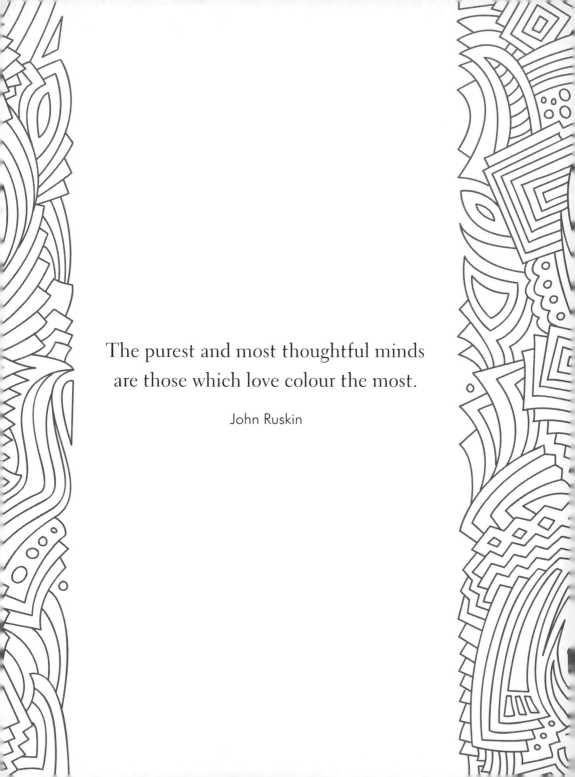

The purest and most thoughtful minds
are those which love colour the most.

John Ruskin

The smallest feline
is a masterpiece.

Leonardo Da Vinci

Nothing makes a house
cosier than cats.

Gladys Taber

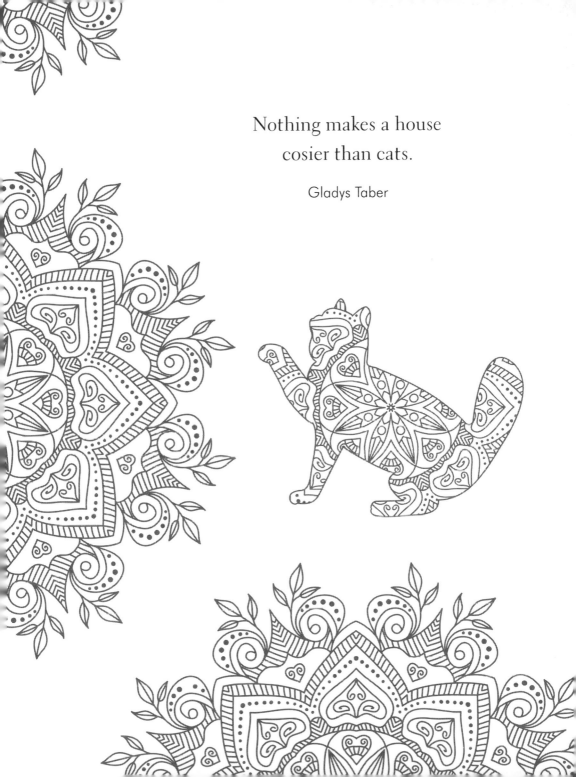

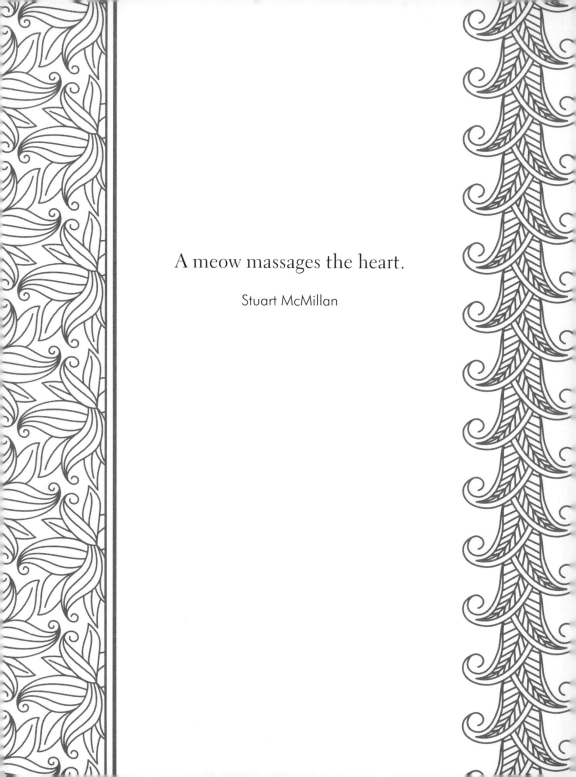

A meow massages the heart.

Stuart McMillan

The world is but a canvas
to our imagination.

Henry David Thoreau

When it comes to knowing how to relax,
cats are the original yoga experts.

Patricia Curtis

I regard cats as one of the great
joys in the world. I see them
as a gift of highest order.

Trisha McCagh

A little drowsing cat is an image
of perfect beatitude.

Jules Champfleury

Daydreaming with pencil and paper is a
respectable form of meditation.

John Howe

Cats are magical… the more you pet
them the longer you both live.

Anonymous

There's no need for a piece of sculpture
in a home that has a cat.

Wesley Bates

A beating heart and an angel's soul, covered in fur.

Lexie Saige

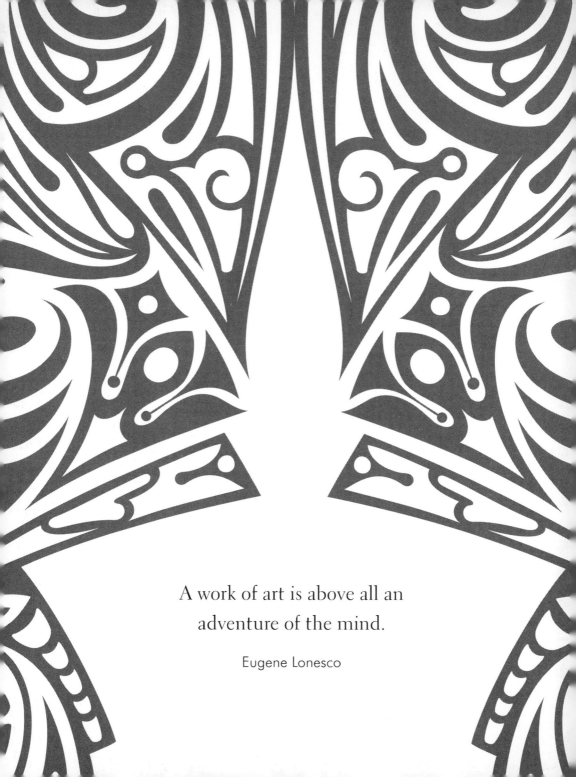

A work of art is above all an
adventure of the mind.

Eugene Lonesco

Cats at fireside live luxuriously and
are the picture of comfort.

Leigh Hunt

Our perfect companions never
have fewer than four feet.

Colette

The extraordinary thing about any cat
is the effect it has on its owner.

Peter Gethers

Art enables us to find ourselves and
lose ourselves at the same time.

Thomas Merton

If a fish is the movement of water embodied, given shape, then cat is a diagram and pattern of subtle air.

Doris Lessing

If there were to be a universal sound depicting peace, I would surely vote for the purr.

Barbara L. Diamond

Like a graceful vase, a cat, even when motionless, seems to flow.

George F. Will

Art is harmony
parallel with nature.

Paul Cézanne

The cat is the animal to whom the Creator
gave the biggest eye, the softest fur, the
most supremely delicate nostrils.

Colette

I believe cats to be spirits come to earth. A cat, I am sure, could walk on a cloud without coming through.

Jules Verne

The cat is nature's beauty.

French proverb

You can't use up creativity.
The more you use, the more you have.

Maya Angelou

If there is one spot of sun
spilling onto the floor, a cat
will find it and soak it up.

Joan Asper McIntosh

Everything a cat is and does physically is to me beautiful, lovely, stimulating, soothing, attractive and an enchantment.

Paul Gallico

A kitten is in the animal
world what a rosebud
is in the garden.

Robert Southey

Art is not a thing, it is a way.

Elbert Hubbard

Happy is the home with at least one cat.

Italian proverb

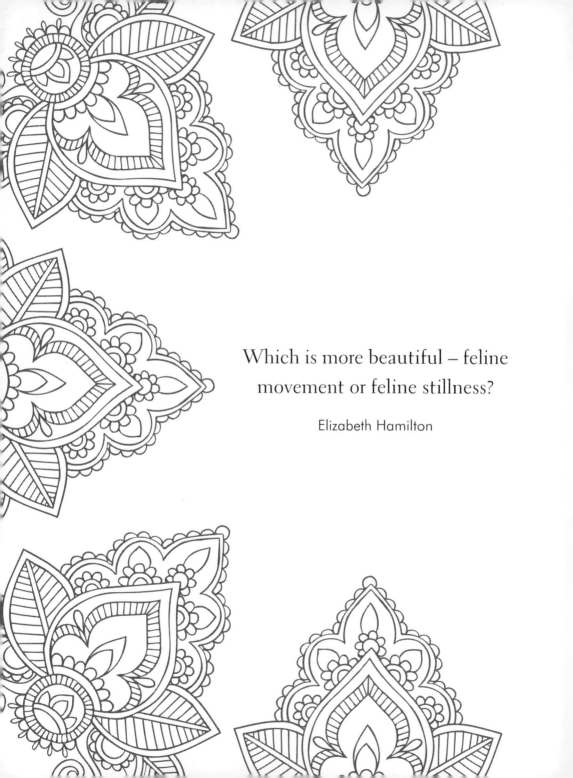

Which is more beautiful – feline movement or feline stillness?

Elizabeth Hamilton

What greater gift than the love of a cat?

Charles Dickens

Colour is like food for the spirit.

Isaac Mizrahi

If you're interested in finding out
more about our products, find us on
Facebook at **HuckAndPucker** and
follow us on Twitter at **@HuckandPucker**.

www.huckandpucker.com